SHIRE NATURAL HISTO

CW00393159

WILLOWS
of the British Isles

THERESA BRENDELL

CONTENTS

COVER: *Dark-leaved Willow (Salix myrsinifolia). These are the male catkins, with long stamens, opening at the same time as the first leaves.*

Series editors: Jim Flegg and Chris Humphries

Set in 9 point Times roman and printed in Great Britain by C. I. Thomas & Sons (Haverfordwest) Ltd, Press Buildings, Merlins Bridge, Haverfordwest, Dyfed.

Introduction

The willows comprise a varied group of trees, shrubs and subshrubs, representatives of which are found throughout Britain. Some species, such as the White and Crack Willows, are quite tall graceful trees with characteristically long narrow leaves, whilst others, notably the sallows, are less prepossessing shrubby bushes or small trees. These are probably best known for their abundant silvery catkins that may appear whilst it is still winter.

Many species are abundant and are readily found wherever waterlogged conditions prevail, whereas others are restricted to a single type of locality. For example, the tiny Least Willow grows only on the higher mountain slopes and Woolly Willow, a very rare plant, hides in just a few remote gullies of the Central Highlands of Scotland. Some willows are planted extensively, for different reasons. The Weeping Willow is an example of an 'amenity' tree, chosen for its pleasing shape to be planted by village ponds, in city parks and suburban gardens, whilst others are planted for more utilitarian purposes, to be made into cricket bats or polo balls. Canes from the osiers are made into baskets of all shapes and sizes.

So many pests devour their leaves, twigs, bark and timber that it is surprising any survive at all. They all grow in wet soils: in marshes, fens and bogs, by rivers, streams, canals, ditches and ponds, in salty slacks and mountain flushes, by the side of motorways, on puddly wasteland and in botanical gardens. They flourish often where other trees and shrubs would drown, binding banks and stabilising unstructured soils. Some of them hybridise so freely that they obscure their parental origins and are the bane of the botanist attempting to name them. They symbolised death and mourning to the earthy and superstitious peoples of the past.

However, beyond a passing appreciation of their general aesthetic merit, most willows are not well known to many people. This book aims to remedy this deficiency by providing a concise appraisal of the genus which contains more native species of tree and woody shrub than any other in Britain.

Willows (genus *Salix*) and poplars (genus *Populus*) together comprise the family Salicaceae. There are about three hundred species of *Salix* throughout the world, distributed mainly in the north temperate and Arctic regions. Some are found in the south temperate regions and the tropics but they are absent from Australasia and the East Indies. The genus *Salix* is usually divided into three subgenera: *Salix*, which contains the true willows (e.g. *S. alba, S. fragilis*); *Vetrix*, the osiers and sallows (e.g. *S. caprea, S. viminalis*); and *Chamaetia*, the dwarf willows (e.g. *S. herbacea, S. reticulata*). Willows are all woody plants, ranging in size from the Least Willow (*S. herbacea*), which is only 1 to 2 centimetres (⅜ to ¾ inch) high, to the more stately White Willow (*S. alba*), which at 25 or even 30 metres (80 to 100 feet) is the tallest willow species in Britain (plate 1). Although they are plants characteristic of damp, wet and marshy areas, some sallows may occur naturally in drier habitats. Willows that are planted deliberately in parks and gardens also flourish in soils that have an average moisture content.

Willows are readily recognised as a group by a number of distinctive characters. The winter buds are protected by a single outer scale and there are no terminal leaf buds. Catkins are borne mostly in late winter and spring, either laterally or terminally on the branches of plants which are either entirely male or entirely female, with the exception of the rare occurrence of mixed sexes in a few hybrids. The catkins are usually erect but in some species are drooping. Both male and female flowers arise in the axil of a single entire scale. Petals and sepals are absent, or possibly represented by one or two small nectaries. The leaves are alternately arranged and are simple in outline.

There are eighteen species native to Britain and twenty-seven interspecific hybrids, which make this group interesting, although often difficult to identify correctly. The sallows in particular present problems as they hybridise very freely. Even infertile hybrids may become well established and spread vegetatively, usually by means of twigs or branches which break off the parent plant and take root.

Willows may be divided into those which occur in suitably damp habitats in lowland Britain and those which are found on the upland moors and mountains of the north and west. The latter group consists of some of the lower-growing sallows and dwarf willows. The lowland species include the taller tree willows, which need the deeper richer soils of these areas, and many sallows and osiers, including the species used for growing canes for basketry. In the past some of these lowland willows were planted to stabilise the banks of waterways and to provide farm animals with fodder, especially in early spring.

Biology of willows

PROPAGATION AND DISPERSAL

Willow seeds are dispersed by wind. They are small and light, enveloped in cottony hairs, and may be carried considerable distances by slight breezes. In any one catkin the seeds are numerous but remain alive only for a few days as they do not contain food reserves. They cannot lie dormant until the occurrence of conditions suitable for germination but must land in a favourable environment during their brief period of viability.

Conditions necessary for successful germination are moisture and an open aspect, such as the wet mud or fine gravel by the side of a stream or pond, or rock crevices where the seeds will not become desiccated. The seedlings are particularly small. Two tiny cotyledons first appear above the ground, followed by two small true leaves arranged oppositely. All subsequent leaves adopt the typical alternate arrangement. Although the germinating seeds have a high moisture requirement, once the plants are established they can grow well in a much drier soil. Because of this dependence of the first stages of growth on wet conditions, however, willows regenerating naturally from seed are restricted to wet areas.

Willows will also grow readily from twigs and are normally cultivated from cuttings simply pushed into suitably prepared ground. In particular, twigs of Crack Willow snap off naturally in high winds and gales at the point of branching. Most of these remain beneath the tree as a distinctive twiggy litter, but those which float off downstream may lodge and take root. Roots can appear within one week of severance and immersion in water.

In wet open meadows circles of Crack Willow can be found, with all the component trees appearing to be of much the same age. It is thought that these circles originated from a single central tree, probably originally cut back to the main stem, a process known as pollarding (plate 2). This was done to encourage the growth of young shoots for livestock. After many years of pollarding, a somewhat top-heavy club-shaped head developed. When pollarding ceased, the weight of the branches caused the old decaying trunk to split and be pulled apart. New trees eventually grew from twigs thus brought into contact with the ground. The old parts of the original tree rotted and a ring of daughter trees was left.

Other species, such as S. repens and the dwarf willows S. herbacea and S. reticulata, spread by means of underground stems, called rhizomes. The area covered by just one plant of S. herbacea can be several square feet and, although growth is extremely slow, a carpet of interwoven twigs gradually forms. In addition to the rhizomatous rooting system, roots also develop from the diminutive branches. The compact growth form of this species largely prevents wind damage.

In contrast, once established, the larger willows and sallows grow quickly: for instance, Cricket Bat Willows (S. alba var. caerulea), which are always propagated from cuttings, attain a girth of 1.5 metres (5 feet) by the time they are twelve years old. Some of the sallows most prized for basketry are also extremely fast growing; the Common Osier (S. viminalis) can produce shoots 2.5 metres (8 feet) long from one cut crown in a year.

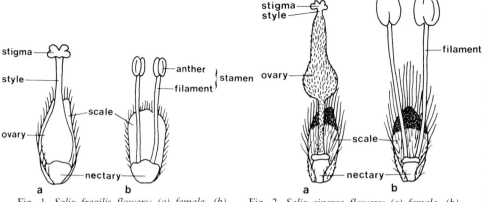

Fig. 1. *Salix fragilis flowers; (a) female, (b) male.*

Fig. 2. *Salix cinerea flowers; (a) female, (b) male.*

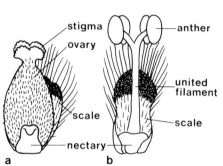

Fig. 3. *Salix purpurea flowers; (a) female, (b) male.*

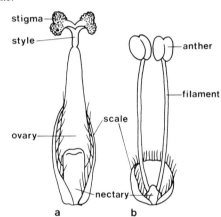

Fig. 4. *Salix herbacea flowers; (a) female, (b) male.*

MORPHOLOGY OF CATKINS

Willow catkins (figs. 1-4, plates 3, 4 and cover) are made up of a central column, or rhachis, bearing numerous single-sexed flowers, each with a basal scale. The overall shape of the catkin is basically cylindrical. The catkins of many species are fairly short, approximately 2 to 3 centimetres (¾ to 1¼ inches) long (although the females extend as the fruits ripen), stiff and erect. Those of the taller willows such as White Willow (*S. alba*), Crack Willow (*S. fragilis*) and their hybrids are more lax and pendant, and those of Creeping Willow (*S. repens*), Downy Willow (*S. lapponum*) and Least Willow (*S. herbacea*) are oval or globose. Within the framework of this general structure,

some features are common to each subgenus whilst others vary according to species, affording a useful aid to identification.

The catkins of true willows (subgenus *Salix*) and sallows and osiers (subgenus *Vetrix*) are borne on short lateral shoots arising from buds formed the previous year. Usually these stalks are leafy, although the leaves may differ in shape and size from the mature summer foliage. Many sallow catkins have very short stalks or are subsessile, with only a few leaves or bracts, except for the female catkins of *S. arbuscula* and *S. myrsinites*, which are borne on long leafy peduncles. Sallow catkins tend to appear before the leaves, as seen in those called pussy

4

Plate 1 (above, left). *Salix alba (White Willow). This is a typical mature white willow, growing in a wet meadow.*
Plate 2 (above, right). *Salix fragilis (Crack Willow). These old trees are evidence of an outdated method of pollarding. It used to be a common sight to see rows of club-headed willows alongside rivers and canals.*
Plate 3 (below). *Salix cinerea (Common Sallow). A honeybee collecting nectar from female catkins. Note the cylindrical shape of the catkins and the leaves just beginning to open.*

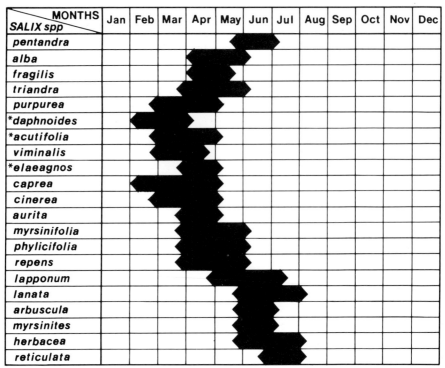

Table 1. *Flowering times of willows. Those marked * are not native to the British Isles but are frequently planted introductions.*

willows, but the true willow catkins open with, or slightly after, the leaves. The third subgenus, *Chamaetia*, the dwarf willows, has catkins that appear after the leaves, from terminal buds on the previous year's growth. Flowering times are given in the table above.

DIVERSITY OF FLORAL PARTS

The flowers have no petals or sepals but there are one or two nectaries thought to represent a vestigial perianth. Sallow flowers of both sexes have one nectary only; all other willows have one or two depending on species. Female flowers have roughly flask-shaped ovaries which enlarge after pollination. The styles may be long, short or completely absent and the stigmas are either two-lobed or entire. Male flowers normally have two stamens, although *S. pentandra* and *S. triandra* usually have five and

three stamens respectively, as their names suggest. In some sallows, for example *S. purpurea* and its hybrids, the stamens may be united along the length of the filament.

The scales differ in each subgenus. Those of true willows are yellowish green and are quickly shed in all species except the Almond Willow (*S. triandra*). In the sallows, osiers and dwarf willows the scales are persistent. Those of sallows and osiers are distinctly two-coloured with a base of pale greenish yellow and tips of either brown or black, whereas dwarf willow scales do not have contrasting tips and may be reddish or brownish in colour. Floral parts of species representing each subgenus are illustrated.

POLLINATION

As male and female catkins are borne on separate plants self-pollination cannot take place. Unusually, cross-pollination is effected by wind and insects. This is in contrast to the closely related poplars, in which wind pollination is the rule. Pollen production is copious, so that when insects, particularly bees and bumble bees, are attracted by the nectar and pollen to alight on a male catkin they are liberally dusted with it. This 'brush blossom' mechanism ensures that the insect's body is well coated with pollen grains from numerous flowers so that when female catkins are visited the likelihood of pollinations between a wide range of different individuals is increased. Although bees are the most important insect visitors, there are others such as true flies, hoverflies and ichneumon flies, species of the last being chiefly responsible for the pollination of Least Willow (*S. herbacea*) at high altitudes. The exposed stamens and stigmas, together with the vast quantities of pollen, also facilitate wind pollination. Willow pollen is small and light, non-sticky and easily carried along in the air flow.

After successful pollination the ovary ripens into a two-valved capsule, which enlarges as the seeds develop. On a dry sunny day the ripe, but still green, capsule splits longitudinally. Beginning at the top of the neck, each half bends back and twists apart spirally, exposing the compressed hairs and eventually pulling apart the two valves. The hairs fan out and separate in the dry air and then a slight breeze is all that is needed to waft each seed free of the catkin (plate 5). The seeds are very small, oblong in shape and approximately 1 millimetre in length. They are released from May to August, varying from one species to another. Although the number of seeds in each capsule is not large — usually less than ten — the number of flowers per catkin and catkins per tree results in such a prodigious quantity of cottony seed that the ground around a grove of sallows can appear as though as light fall of snow has occurred.

FOLIAGE

Willows are renowned for the variability of their leaves, although this is more pronounced in some species than others. All the leaves are simple and are almost exclusively alternate in arrangement, the exception being *S. purpurea*, which has

Fig. 5 (below, left). *The position of dehiscing fruits on a catkin of Salix cinerea (Common Sallow).*
Fig. 6 (below, right). *Capsule of Salix cinerea splitting and twisting to release seeds.*
Fig. 7 (right). *Salix cinerea seed.*

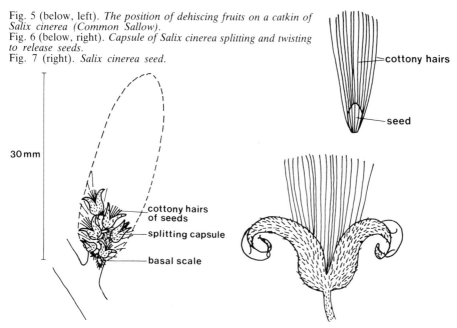

30 mm

cottony hairs of seeds

splitting capsule

basal scale

cottony hairs

seed

some of its leaves arranged oppositely. Generally leaf shape ranges from the lanceolate (spear-shaped) leaves of *S. fragilis*, *S. alba* and *S. viminalis* to the almost round leaves of *S. reticulata*. Between these two extremes there is an assortment of elliptical, oblong, ovate (teardrop) and obovate (inverted teardrop) shapes, many of which occur in the same species. The foliage of *S. alba*, *S. aurita*, *S. cinerea* and *S. phylicifolia* is illustrated in plates 6-9.

GROWTH AND SHAPE

Each species has its own characteristic pattern of branching and growth, within which, in optimum environmental conditions, different individuals assume a roughly similar shape. Some of these characters, such as the arrangement of the leaves and the angle at which the branches diverge, are independent of external factors. The rate of growth and ultimate size of the plant are affected by unfavourable conditions, especially the harsh climate experienced on exposed mountainsides. For example, *S. aurita*, which in lowland or sheltered localities forms shrubs up to 3 metres (10 feet), forms stunted dwarves of less than 1 metre (3 feet 3 inches) when subjected to prolonged exposure to wind and low temperatures. The smaller mountain sallows such as *S. arbuscula* and *S. myrsinites* grow into upright shrubs on the more sheltered slopes and can have a completely prostrate growth form in the bleaker positions.

Pollarding or pruning a willow alters its shape but it also affects the character of those branches which subsequently arise from the trimmed parts. They tend to be longer, straighter, with fewer side shoots and often bearing much larger leaves than usual.

The angle of branching is more conspicuous in the larger species as these are more often left to grow unchecked. Typical of *S. alba* is a graceful upswept crown whose branches diverge at the rather narrow angle of 30 to 50 degrees (plate 10). In contrast, *S. fragilis* has a much broader crown with branches arising at an angle of 60 to 90 degrees (plate 11); at maturity this crown becomes somewhat open in appearance as twigs and small branches tend to break off in high winds. *S. pentandra*, the Bay Willow, grows into a small tree with a quite different, broad low crown, which, when its leaves are fully open, appears dense and dark green. *S. triandra* and all the larger sallows are usually robust shrubs although some will grow into small trees if not pruned or pollarded. *S. cinerea* and *S. caprea* have fairly erect branches with stout twigs but the osiers *S. viminalis* and *S. purpurea* are much more graceful with long straight slender twigs.

MATURE BARK

The bark of all except one of the willows and larger sallows is greyish brown and becomes fissured with age (plates 12 and 13). The exception is *S. triandra*, which has a smooth bark that peels off in patches. This characteristic is also seen in some of its hybrids, for example *S. triandra* × *S. viminalis* (*S.* × *mollissima*).

WINTER TWIGS

Another pleasing feature of some willows is the colour of the young twigs in their first winter. These are stocked by garden centres especially for their decorative value. Species which possess this trait include *S. acutifolia*, which has violet twigs, and *S. chermesina*, whose twigs are bright vermilion. Both these are introductions. The native *S. alba* var. *vitellina* has twigs of bright yellow or orange.

Growth in waterlogged conditions

Species of *Salix* are often the first woody plants to become established in wet habitats. Although they are often dominant in such areas, this may be transitory, with other shrubs and trees displacing them as the ground becomes drier. Waterlogged soils may be poor in nutrients and can have very low levels of oxygen, especially in static water. In these conditions toxic compounds collect

Plate 4. *Salix* x *sepulcralis (Weeping Willow). This hybrid bears both male and female catkins on the same tree.*

Plate 5. *Salix cinerea (Common Sallow). Ripe capsules splitting to release their cottony seeds.*

Plate 6. *Salix alba (White Willow). The pale colour of these leaves is due to the numerous closely appressed hairs present on both surfaces.*

9

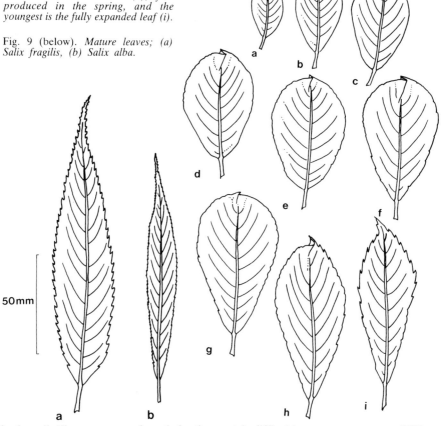

Fig. 8 (right). *Variability of foliage. Nine leaves taken from a twig of Salix cinerea picked in southern Scotland in mid June. The oldest is (a), first produced in the spring, and the youngest is the fully expanded leaf (i).*

Fig. 9 (below). *Mature leaves; (a) Salix fragilis, (b) Salix alba.*

50mm

in the soil. These are caused partly by the metabolic processes of anaerobic bacteria, many of which produce hydrogen sulphide as a waste product, and partly by the incomplete decomposition of organic matter. Toxic products also accumulate internally, within the roots of plants trying to grow in waterlogged environments, because in the absence of adequate oxygen, only a restricted respiratory metabolism can take place. Instead of the evolution of carbon dioxide and water, ethanol, acetaldehyde and ethylene are produced.

For a plant to grow in such conditions, it has to possess characteristics, usually anatomical, by which these environmen-

tal difficulties are overcome. Willows compensate for the low concentrations of oxygen and nutrients around their submerged parts by the production of long adventitious roots, which spread out into the water. These may be extremely numerous and may greatly increase the surface area through which oxygen and minerals can be absorbed. They are pink or white and are the first kind of roots to grow from detached floating twigs. Not all species have been observed to produce these roots, but those which customarily establish themselves in very wet conditions, for example White, Crack and Purple Willows, do so.

The deleterious metabolites formed

10

when the normal biochemical pathways of respiration are impeded are expelled by being passed up through the xylem from the roots to the leaves, where they diffuse out. It has also been shown that the lenticels of willow twigs have a dual function. In addition to the diffusion of atmospheric oxygen into the plant, ethanol, acetaldehyde and ethylene are excreted out through the lenticels. This is an interesting contrast to the poplars, where such a function has not been demonstrated.

Identification of willows

It is often considered that willows and sallows are difficult to identify. This is not because their morphological attributes are necessarily more confusing than those of any other group, but largely because it is not possible to collect or examine all the features required for identification from the same plant at one visit. Ideally, identifications should be based on male and female catkins and mature leaves. This is not easy to achieve and not always possible and errors can occur when attempting to match up both sexes of catkin with mature foliage. Trees of each sex do not necessarily occur in the same vicinity. Also, male catkins fall as soon as they have shed their pollen, so they are only available for inspection for a short time early in the year. Species characteristics of the floral parts include the presence or absence of hairs and their proportions, but as there is some variability within the species it requires experience and knowledge of the genus before it is possible to identify an individual from its catkins alone.

Despite the variation encountered in the leaves, they are the best guide to the identity of a willow. It is very important to examine the mature foliage. Leaves that are produced in spring and early summer can be extremely misleading as they may differ considerably in shape, size and margin detail from those appearing later. In some species, for example *S. cinerea*, this is especially noticeable.

Leaves of *S. alba* and *S. fragilis*, although distinct when mature, may be difficult to tell apart when immature. Their shape and size are similar, both may be hairy to a greater or lesser extent, and the colour of both varies. By mid June, however, the *alba* foliage has remained fairly small — 5 to 10 centimetres (2 to 4 inches) long. It has extremely fine serrations along the margin and so many silky white appressed hairs on both leaf surfaces that it appears a very pale bluish green. The mature leaves of *fragilis* are larger — 6 to 16 centimetres (2¼ to 6¼ inches) long — hairless, with coarsely toothed margins, a bright or dark green on the upper surface and paler on the lower.

Species such as *S. myrsinifolia* and *S. repens* exhibit a wide range of leaf shape even when mature. In order to minimise the problems created by this variation, leaves should be selected from branches of normal growth, avoiding those arising from a pollarded crown or those growing in shade. These leaves are often abnormally large and atypical.

Table 2 presents a simplified key to all eighteen native species, together with three of the most frequently planted introductions. It is based on mature foliage characteristics. For the sake of clarity and brevity, hybrids and varieties have been omitted.

Four species are judged to exist in forms sufficiently different to warrant division into varieties. *S. fragilis* occurs in Britain in four recognised varieties, *fragilis*, *furcata*, *russelliana* and *decipiens*; *S. alba* as three varieties, *alba*, *vitellina* and *caerulea*; and *S. triandra* as two, *triandra* and *hoffmanniana*. The only sallow subdivided in this way is *S. caprea*, which has a variety *sphacelata*, but *S. cinerea* is subdivided into two subspecies, ssp. *cinerea* and ssp. *oleifolia*. Ssp. *cinerea* is found in eastern England and differs from ssp. *oleifolia* in its very hairy twigs, more bushy habit and ashy grey tinge to the foliage. Ssp. *oleifolia* is the more widespread of the two and has rust-red hairs on the underside of the dark green leaves.

With practice and careful comparison it becomes easier to identify most species and to be able to detect the hybrids.

Plate 7. *Salix aurita (Eared Sallow). This species has pubescent, blue-green leaves. The large persistent stipules can be seen here.*

Plate 8. *Salix cinerea ssp oleifolia (Common Sallow). The leaves of Common Sallow are leathery and dark green. The presence of small red hairs makes them look rather dull.*

Plate 9. *Salix phylicifolia (Tea-leaved Willow). The leaves of this shrub are bright green and glossy.*

12

Plate 10. *Salix alba (White Willow).*
This photograph was taken in
spring, before the leaves had fully
opened, and shows the graceful form
of the narrowly spreading branches.

Plate 11. *Salix fragilis (Crack Wil-*
low). This photograph, also taken in
spring, shows in contrast the more
widely spreading branches of this
species.

Hybridisation in willows

After many differences of opinion, it is generally agreed today that there are eighteen native species growing in the British Isles. The reason disagreements on the number of species arose and were perpetuated amongst botanists of the late eighteenth and early nineteenth centuries was the reluctance of some to accept the fact that many of the described species were hybrids. Eventually it was elucidated that not only did hybridisation occur but that its occurrence was widespread. Further to this, it was realised that between some species hybridisation and backcrossing was so extensive that a complete gradation of intermediate forms existed.

The phenomenon of hybridisation is now widely acknowledged and has been the subject of more sophisticated analyses than were possible in previous centuries. The willow hybrids considered here are interspecific; that is, they are the resultant progeny of a successful crossing of a male of one species of *Salix* with a female of another. Many such crossings have occurred spontaneously, and although the parentage of some has been unravelled, that of others, especially when there have been repeated crossings involving more than two species, is not clear.

Hybrids may or may not be fertile. In a group such as *Salix,* where propagation by vegetative means is commonplace, infertility is not necessarily a deterrent to the successful spread of such a hybrid and may even be advantageous. Alternatively, when progeny are fertile there may be repeated backcrossings with either or both parents. This has occurred to such an extent between some species, notably *S. caprea* × *S. cinerea, S. aurita* × *S. cinerea* and *S. myrsinifolia* × *S. phylicifolia,* that all stages of transition between each parent exist and it may be impossible to ascribe certain identity to an individual.

To complicate matters further, some hybrids also cross with a third and possibly even more species. Not all crosses result in fertile hybrids of both sexes. In some instances progeny of one sex only is produced, the other sex appearing very rarely, if at all, for example *S. cinerea* × *S. viminalis,* which produces a predominantly female hybrid. If vegetative reproduction occurs naturally or artificially, a one-sex clone is formed. It is thought theoretically possible for all the British species of *Salix* to hybridise, directly or indirectly, but with one or two exceptions, for example *S. triandra* × *S. purpurea* and *S. triandra* × *S. viminalis,* species from the subgenus *Salix* do not hybridise with those from the other two subgenera.

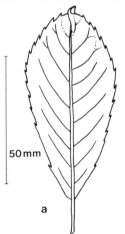
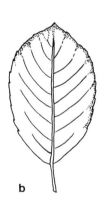
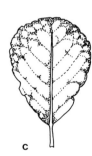

50mm

a b c

Fig. 10. *Mature leaves of Salix cinerea (a), Salix aurita (c) and the hybrid Salix x multinervis (b). The hybrid is intermediate in size and shape between its two parents.*

SUBGENUS	SALIX									VETRIX									CHAMAETIA		
	pentandra	*alba*	*fragilis*	*triandra*	*purpurea*	**daphnoides*	** acutifolia*	*viminalis*	** elaeagnos*	*caprea*	*cinerea*	*aurita*	*repens*	*phylicifolia*	*myrsinifolia*	*arbuscula*	*lapponum*	*lanata*	*myrsinites*	*herbacea*	*reticulata*
Tree taller than 10 m		●	●																		
Shrub 2-10 m	●			●	●	●	●	●	●	●	●	●		●	●						
Shrub or sub-shrub less than 2 m													●			●	●	●	●	●	●
One-year-old twig pubescent											●				○		●				
One-year-old twig not pubescent	●	●	●	●	●	●	●	●	●	●		●	●	●	○	●	●		●	●	●
Stipules present				●			●	●	●	●	●	●			○		●	●			
Stipules soon falling, absent	●	●	●		●			●	●				●	●		●	●		○	●	●
Leaf shape very variable													●		●						
Leaf shape lanceolate	○	●	●	●	●	●	●		○		●		●	●	●		●				
Leaf shape ovate	●										●		●	●		●	○		●		
Leaf shape obovate							●				●	●			●	●		●		○	
Leaf shape oblong, elliptic	●					○			○		○		●	●		●			●		
Leaf shape round																		○		●	●
Leaf apex acuminate		●	●	○	●	●	●	●	●							○					
Leaf apex acute or cuspidate	●			●	●						●	○	●	●	●	●	●	○			
Leaf apex obtuse										●	●		●			○		●			
Leaf apex rounded												●								●	●
Leaf margin entire								●	●	○	○	○	○	○			●	●			●
Leaf margin serrate or crenate	●	○	●	●	●	●				○	○		○	●	●	●			●	●	
Leaf margin undulate												●				○	○				
Upper surface bright green								●					○	●		●			●	●	
Upper surface dark green	●		●	●	●	●			●		●			●		●					●
Upper surface pale or blue green		●											●	●			●				
Upper surface hairy		●								○			●	●		●	●				
Upper surface not hairy	●		●	●	●	●	●	●	●		●		●	●	●	●			●	●	●
Lower surface hairy		●						●	●	●	●	●	●		○	●	●	●	●	●	○
Lower surface not hairy	●		●	●	●	●	●							●		●			●	●	
Leaf wrinkled												●									●
Catkins before leaves					●	●		●	●	●	●	●	○	●							
Catkins with leaves	●	●	●	●			●			○	●	●	●	●		●	●		●		
Catkins after leaves																				●	●

* Introduced species frequently planted for their showy catkins or coloured twigs.

● Character present.

○ Character either present sometimes, or present to a certain extent.

Column descriptions (left to right):
- *pentandra*: Young leaves very fragrant; twigs very glossy.
- *alba*: Leaves very pale; undersurface white.
- *fragilis*: Twigs snap off readily at junction.
- *triandra*: Bark smooth, peeling off in patches.
- *purpurea*: Bark tastes very bitter.
- **daphnoides*: Young twigs with dense bloom; leathery leaves.
- **acutifolia*: Leaves very narrow; twigs violet in winter.
- *viminalis*: Margins of leaves rolled downwards.
- **elaeagnos*: Extremely linear leaves; conspicuous cottony hairs, lower leaf.
- *caprea*: Leaves soft to touch, woolly underneath.
- *cinerea*: Ssp. *cinerea*: twigs very hairy. Ssp. *oleifolia*: rust-red hairs on leaves.
- *aurita*: Blue-green leaves, stipules large.
- *repens*: Creeping growth with extensive rhizomes.
- *phylicifolia*: Dark, rather leathery leaves.
- *myrsinifolia*: Leaves turn black when dried.
- *arbuscula*: Prostrate or ascending branches from base.
- *lapponum*: Hairs on both sides of leaf; upper surface dark grey/green.
- *lanata*: Young growth and all leaves very woolly.
- *myrsinites*: Both leaf surfaces bright green and shiny.
- *herbacea*: Very small, spreading plant 0-30 mm.
- *reticulata*: Conspicuous venation, impressed above.

WHY HYBRIDS HAPPEN

Current opinion supports the theory that even closely related species normally maintain themselves as discrete entities by the operation of barriers which prevent hybridisation. In general, these are sexual incompatibility, differences in flowering time and geographical separation, which is sufficiently great distances between individuals to prevent pollen of one species reaching the stigmas of another. Successful crossings occur when one or all of these barriers become ineffectual.

The removal of a geographical barrier is a frequent cause for the appearance of hybrids. This may happen when one or both future parents, hitherto growing in regions separate from one another, undergo a change in distribution so that they overlap. Such changes can take place following a drift in environmental tolerance, a natural change in environment or climatic conditions, or, increasingly, widespread alterations to habitat caused by human activity and the deliberate planting by man of individuals of a species outside its normal range. When the two species now living adjacently have compatible pollen and flowers which mature, at least in some years, synchronously, the plants may indeed hybridise.

As well as these spontaneous hybrids, there are 'artificial' hybrids, which are crosses that have been made purposely by people such as horticulturalists, botanists and geneticists. An artificial hybrid was bred in Sweden by N. H. Nilsson in the 1950s which is said to have had in its parentage thirteen different species.

However, the most famous example of an artificial *Salix* hybrid must be the Weeping Willow (plate 14). It is a particularly ornamental and well-known tree commonly planted by ponds, rivers and streams and in parks and gardens in lowland areas. For many years it was thought to be a pendulous variety of White Willow and as such has received a number of different names: *S. alba* 'tristis', *S. alba* 'chryscoma', *S. chrysocoma* and *S. alba* var. *vitellina* 'pendula'. It is now known to be a hybrid between a variety of White Willow, *S. alba* var. *vitellina*, and a species native to western China, *S. babylonica*. This species was introduced to Europe and eventually to England in the eighteenth century, where its attractive pendulous habit made it popular. Unfortunately, it was not suited to the British climate and did not flourish. The hybrid was probably made in Germany, where the earliest record of Weeping Willow is found in the 1888 catalogue of a Berlin horticulturalist. It is now correctly named *S.* × *sepulcralis,* and although there is now a perplexing array of *babylonica* × *alba* hybrids, *S.* × *sepulcralis* nothovar. *chrysocoma* is the most popular. This variety has inherited the native hardiness and characteristic golden colour from *S. alba* var. *vitellina* and the sweeping branches from *S. babylonica*. It is not a fertile hybrid: female trees are not known although female catkins are sometimes found on predominantly male trees. Propagation is therefore always from cuttings.

OCCURRENCE OF NATURAL HYBRIDS

Over one hundred hybrids between the British species have been recorded, although only twenty-seven have been verified in Britain. There is also doubt and confusion attached to the authenticity of some of these records. However, even if these more dubious crosses are ignored, there still remains a large number of hybrid willows. Some of these are extremely rare and are most unlikely to be encountered. Therefore only some of the most common and important hybrids, most of which are also mentioned elsewhere in this book, will be dealt with here.

Most hybrids do not have a vernacular name and are known either by their parentage, for example *S. caprea* × *S. cinerea,* or by a binary name consisting of the generic name *Salix* and a specially ascribed hybrid name, for example *reichardtii,* separated by a multiplication sign to signify that the plant is a cross.

Many of the better known and more widespread hybrids are good osiers, that is plants suitable for the production of canes, and as such have often been cultivated. They include *S. triandra* × *S. viminalis* (*S.* × *mollissima*) and *S. purpurea* × *S. viminalis* (*S.* × *rubra*). *S.* ×

16

Plate 12 (above, left). *Salix alba (White Willow). Detail of bark, showing the coarse diamond-shaped fissures. Crack Willow bark may be confused with it, but this species has a more linear pattern.*
Plate 13 (above, right). *Salix caprea (Goat Willow). Young trees just beginning to develop mature bark show an attractive intermediate stage, when the fissures appear as small diamond shapes.*
Plate 14 (below). *Salix x sepulcralis, Weeping Willow, in spring, showing the very long pendulous branches.*

mollissima exists in two fairly constant forms but *S.* × *rubra* exists as a gradated series between each parent. *S. cinerea* × *S. viminalis* (*S.* × *smithiana*) may also have been used for canes. Plants of this hybrid with male catkins do not occur very often so it is thought that it must have been spread vegetatively.

S. caprea × *S. cinerea* × *S. viminalis* (*S.* × *calodendron*) is an example of a hybrid which is quite well-known and widespread in hedgerows and on waste ground, but whose parentage is still open to some doubt. *S. caprea* × *S. cinerea* (*S.* × *reichardtii*), *S. aurita* × *S. cinerea* (*S.* × *multinervis*) and *S. aurita* × *S. repens* (*S.* × *ambigua*) are hybrids which occur wherever the parents are found together and they make identification difficult, especially in the case of *S.* × *reichardtii*, which comprises a series of intermediates. *S.* × *multinervis* more consistently exhibits certain characters from both parents. Another example of two species whose hybrid backcrosses is *S. myrsinifolia* and *S. phylicifolia*. *S.* × *tetrapla* forms such an extensive and finely graduated series of intermediates that the two parents are completely joined, forming what is probably the most difficult series of willows in Britain.

Those species growing at higher altitudes, including the rare calcicoles, also hybridise with each other and with the more ubiquitous species when there is overlap, for example, the Least Willow, *S. herbacea*, hybridises with both *S. aurita* and *S. repens*; and *S. lapponum* also hybridises with *S. aurita*.

Ecology

Willows of one species or another can be found the length and breadth of Britain in almost all types of wet habitat. The natural distribution of some of these, particularly White and Crack Willows and some sallows in lowland areas, has been obscured by their deliberate planting in the past to prevent erosion of riverbanks and for cane production. Additionally, some hybrids, particularly those which are fertile and which repeatedly backcross, may form hybrid swarms, which can confuse the boundaries of the parent species. This has occurred in all three groups of willow.

As a general rule, the tallest species require deep rich soils and for that reason tend to be more common in the south and east of England, where the land is flattest and the soils most suitable. The very low-growing or dwarf species are able to prosper on the thin wet soils of the mountains in the north and west. However, White and Crack Willows can grow tall and well in the north, except in the extreme north-west of Scotland, succeeding wherever the soil conditions are right. Frequently, White and Crack Willows and their hybrids are the only tall trees found in a waterside community, although poplars and alders sometimes grow in association with them.

Two other willows, Bay Willow (*S. pentandra*) and Almond Willow (*S. triandra*), also grow into trees, although smaller ones that seldom exceed 10 metres (33 feet). They have similar habitat preferences, growing by streams, rivers and in marshes and wet woods. Bay Willow has a more northerly distribution than Almond Willow and is found in the north-west, as far north as Sutherland in Scotland. Almond Willow only reaches south-east Scotland, where it is local in distribution; it is rare in Wales, preferring the more eastern counties of England, but is also found in southern Ireland. Both species have been planted outside their natural range, especially *S. triandra*, as this species is a good osier.

Many sallows are not exacting in their requirements and are found in a wide range of wet habitats. In particular, *S. caprea*, *S. cinerea* and *S. aurita* grow abundantly throughout the British Isles, together with their hybrids, which are also plentiful. Goat Willow (*S. caprea*) is seen by roadside ditches and on heathlands, commons and in woods all over Britain, sometimes forming copses on the wetter areas, although this species will also tolerate drier conditions than other sallows. The Common Sallow (*S. cinerea*) is equally profuse and in East Anglia is one of the first woody shrubs to become established in drying reedswamp. As the swamp dries further, alder takes over, and a successional progression can be traced.

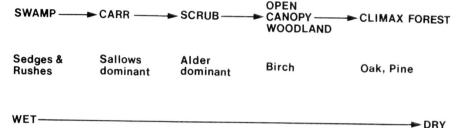

Fig. 11. *The range of preferred habitats of a variety of flora, showing the relative position of sallows.*

Both *S. caprea* and *S. cinerea* tolerate altitudes up to almost 900 metres (3000 feet) and quite acid conditions. *S. aurita* (Eared Sallow), although similarly found all over Britain, tends to be even more tolerant of wet acid conditions, forming small groves on mountainsides, and also seems able to tolerate a certain amount of salt in the environment as this species can be found beside the sea and salt lochs in Scotland. It is one of the very few sallows that can grow in the extreme north of Scotland and in the Shetland Isles, where it is found occasionally as a component of ungrazed scrub.

These three species can also be found as constituents of the scrub or understorey layer in woodland, particularly in the more waterlogged patches where other trees cannot make good growth. In Scottish woods of birch, rowan, aspen and alder, Eared and Common Sallow grow; in Irish woodlands of oak and birch and in English ash and oak woods, Goat Willow and Common Sallow grow in the understorey.

Only from the southern beechwoods are sallows absent, partly because beech tends to grow on higher, drier ground than other forest trees and partly because the canopy of beechwoods is so dense that very few shrubs can grow in its shade.

The last common and widespread sallow is the Common Osier (*S. viminalis*). This is a species that is restricted to lower altitudes than *aurita*, *cinerea* and *caprea*. With its distinctively long, very narrow leaves it is easier to recognise than other sallows, although its hybrids, especially with Purple Willow (*S. purpurea*), may be mistaken for it. Purple Willow (plate

15) is not so widespread although in areas where it does occur it may be present in abundance. *S. purpurea*, *S. viminalis* and their hybrid, *S. × rubra*, are all examples of osiers whose natural ranges have been obscured by planting for basket making.

S. repens (Creeping Willow) also occurs in most parts of the British Isles but it too is local in distribution. It grows on damp heath and moorland and is also commonly found near the sea in areas of sand dunes. The way in which dunes develop results in the formation of successive ridges of dry sand separated by valleys known as 'slacks', which are moist and may contain permanent pools. The dune system is a hostile environment as the sand is unstabilised, poor in nutrients such as nitrogen and extremely dry on the ridges. The plants which manage to colonise the dunes, and therefore stabilise the loose sand, form a well documented and specialised community, the best known component of which is Marram Grass.

Creeping Willow becomes established in the wet slacks and contributes towards the stabilisation of the dunes. It grows into a low dense bushy shrub, up to 1 metre (3 feet 3 inches) in height, which spreads into the dry dunes by means of rhizomes. Water is supplied to all parts of the plant by those roots which remain anchored in the waterlogged slacks. Gradually this willow forms a covering of vegetation over the sand which prevents wind and rain erosion. The accumulation of detritus beneath these plants also contributes to soil formation and an improved nutritional status. As in the case of Marram Grass, if more loose sand is blown on top of Creeping Willow it can

Plate 15. *Salix purpurea (Purple Willow). This species, here growing amongst other shrubs on a riverbank, is one of the three most often cultivated for cane production.*

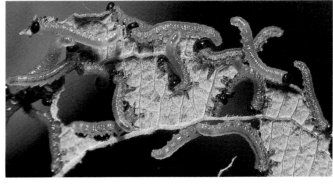

Plate 16. *Nematus spp on sallow leaves. Sawfly caterpillars are often present in large numbers and reduce many of the leaves to 'skeletons'.*

grow up through it.

The range of *S. repens*, like that of *S. aurita*, extends to the Shetlands. However, neither species is particularly common in this northerly locality and a hybrid between the two, *S. × ambigua*, is more successful and widespread here than either parent.

Tea-leaved Willow (*S. phylicifolia*) and Dark-leaved Willow (*S. myrsinifolia*) are not as widespread and are found naturally only in northern England, Ireland and Scotland as far north as the Outer Hebrides and the Orkneys, where their distribution is rather patchy and they are not common species. They both grow by streams and pools in lowland areas and are also found up to 900 metres (3000 feet), where their range overlaps with that of the mountain willows. They hybridise very freely in places where they occur together, and in some places such as the Shetlands this hybrid, *S. × tetrapla*, has been planted.

The three remaining sallows, *S. arbuscula*, *S. lapponum* and *S. lanata*, and three dwarf willows, *S. myrsinites*, *S. herbacea* and *S. reticulata*, are all found at high altitudes. *S. lanata*, *S. arbuscula*, *S. myrsinites* and *S. reticulata* are rare and are all restricted to a few places in Scotland on wet basic rocks.

S. myrsinites, *S. lapponum* and *S. myrsinifolia* can be found as patches of low-growing scrub, often quite dense, which on mountainsides is kept short by the action of the wind. These species, together with *S. phylicifolia*, are also found as a characteristic community growing in little mountainside flushes. They form one stage of a succession of plants which initially develops on bare, continuously wet rock. First, algae, liverworts and mosses colonise the rock. This eventually results in a sufficient accumulation of detritus for small herbaceous plants to invade. As the humus layer continues to grow, more shrubby species can take hold, including *S. myrsinites* (only on basic rocks), *S. lapponum* and *S. phylicifolia*. The growth of these plants forms a gradually extending platform upon which more humus collects. This is a somewhat transitory structure which may collapse in the event of a sudden large flush of water. The sequence may then begin again on the bare rock.

The rarest willows grow on the inaccessible cliffs and ledges and in the gullies of the Grampian Highlands, although only where basic rocks are exposed. Their scarcity is due to various reasons, possibly the most influential of which is that there is only a very limited area of calcareous rock in the Scottish Highlands. On these outcrops grazing pressure restricts them still further. Additionally, some of them are at the edge of their natural range in Scotland, notably the Woolly Willow (*S. lanata*), which is the rarest of all. It is an Arctic species, whose range is Scandinavia, Arctic and sub-Arctic Europe and Asia, unlike *S. myrsinites*, *S. arbuscula* and *S. reticulata*, which are more widespread and are found on central and southern European mountain ranges, as well as in Scandinavia and Arctic and sub-Arctic Europe and Russia.

The Least Willow (*S. herbacea*) is different in distribution and within its range is not uncommon. It is found on most of the high mountains of Wales, the Lake District, Ireland and Scotland, growing up to 1300 metres (4250 feet). It is usually found only on the higher slopes, above the levels at which other shrubs and most other herbaceous plants can grow, although in parts of Sutherland it has been recorded as low as 100 metres (330 feet). It is indifferent to the nature of the underlying rock, growing well on both acidic and basic types. Soils are usually thin and poor on the high mountainsides where it is found and its matlike branching habit helps to prevent erosion. The climatic conditions are harsh, with high winds and rainfall, low temperatures and snow cover for much of the year. Growth is slow but as few other plants survive these conditions it does not have to compete with and is not overtopped by taller species. These miniature subshrubs are thought to live for an extremely long time.

Pests and diseases

Willows and sallows are host to a huge array of insects, in terms of both numbers of species and numbers of individuals that are recorded as feeding on them.

Fig. 12. *Salix herbacea (Least Willow). The smallest and hardiest willow, it endures conditions so harsh that little else except lichens and the moss Rhacomitrium lanuginosum can survive. The ripening female catkins can be seen here.*

Many of these insects are not specific to willows and feed equally well on other trees and shrubs, but there are those which live exclusively on willows. It is not yet fully understood why willows have so many insect 'predators' or even if all *Salix* species are consumed equally. Factors thought to be involved include the nature of the chemicals deposited in the leaves and bark, the presence or absence of hairs on the leaves and the appearance of leaves early in the spring. Whatever the reasons, willows harbour more insect pests than any other British tree except the oak.

So many different lepidopteran caterpillars feed on *Salix* that it seems remarkable that willows are not all completely defoliated by this order of insects alone. In Britain, these are virtually all moth larvae and include over 150 of the larger species. Some of these caterpillars are brightly coloured and conspicuous, such as the Yellowtail Moth (*Euproctis similis*), the Emperor Moth (*Saturnia pavonia*) and the Lackey Moth (*Malacosoma neustria*). The last species is colonial and may be present on sallows in such large numbers that the bushes are defoliated. Others are bizarre like the strange caterpillars of the Eyed Hawk-moth, or are camouflaged by their dull coloration.

Bugs (order Hemiptera) are to be found in quantity, including the aphids *Herocomma populea* and *Melanoxantherum salicis*, which can build up populations sufficiently great to kill the host tree. A smaller number of beetle species (order Coleoptera) are found, mainly members of the phytophagous family Chrysomelidae. Some of these feed exclusively on *Salix*, for example *Lochmaea capreae* and *Chalcoides plutus*.

Sawflies (order Hymenoptera) are abundant. They include those which cause the formation of red leaf galls (*Pontania proxima* and *P. viminalis*), and others, for example *Nematus* spp, whose larvae cause serious defoliation (plate 16). A smaller number of true flies (order Diptera) and grasshoppers (order Orthoptera) may also be found.

FUNGAL DISEASES

Willows are attacked by a number of fungi, whose effects vary in severity and importance. Some attack the leaves and young twigs, for instance *Venturia chlorospora*, which causes willow scab, a disease that is particularly serious in wet weather, when it may cause the loss of all leaves. Others rot the heartwood of the main branches and trunk. These include several species of bracket fungi. Those which infect cultivated willows and sallows can be very detrimental to their economic value. Amongst these are the rust fungi *Melampsora* spp, which attacks osiers, making the canes useless for basketry.

A bacterium, *Erwinia salicis*, causes Watermark Disease in Cricket Bat Willow. As well as affecting the general health of the tree by causing die-back, it causes deep discoloration of the timber, making it unfit for bat making.

Uses of willow wood

Although willows have never been considered as a major timber producer, the characteristic properties of willow wood have made it ideally suited to some specialised and diverse uses. It gives a soft but light and tough timber with a high resistance to splintering when subjected to impaction stresses. It has been used to make cricket bats, polo balls, boxes, steamer paddles, tool handles, brake blocks of railway rolling stock, artificial limbs and milkmaid's yokes. Some of these uses are now of no more than historical interest, but the wood is still prized for the making of cricket bats. The other major craft industry associated with willow is the use of year-old canes for wickerwork items such as baskets and lobster pots. Another mainly rural use is for fences, which are made from cleft poles a few years old.

MANUFACTURE OF CRICKET BATS

Cricket bats are made from the Cricket Bat Willow (*S. alba* var. *caerulea*), which is always propagated from cuttings or 'sets'. These are planted about 6 metres

(20 feet) apart. All branches on the lower 2.5 metres (8 feet) of trunk are removed to prevent knot formation in the timber. On good soil growth is rapid and they may reach marketable size within twelve years. By this time they are about 1.5 metres (5 feet) in circumference. The trunk is then cut into lengths 800 millimetres (31 inches) long and each of these is split into up to eight segments. These clefts are seasoned and then shaped to form the blade of a bat, orientated so that the face which strikes the ball lies along the radius of the bole. This ensures strength, resistance to impact and freedom from warping.

BASKETRY

Basket making is an ancient craft. In Britain it has been dated back to 100 BC from fragments found in Somerset. It used to be an extremely important skill although its value has declined since the advent of so many modern materials from which baskets, crates and boxes can be made. Nonetheless, objects from willow canes are light, hard-wearing and attractive, ensuring that basket making continues to retain its status of a rural industry.

In Britain's oceanic climate willows and osiers were not, in the past, grown in plantations, as there were sufficient to be found growing wild, although particularly prized strains would have been cultivated to some extent. Canes have been obtained from many species of willow and sallow but Common Osier (*S. viminalis*), Almond Willow (*S. triandra*) and Purple Willow (*S. purpurea*) are thought to be best. Varieties of these three species are now cultivated commercially Propagation is from cuttings taken from one-year-old willow rods planted in spring. Each winter they are cut back to ground level although this harvest is not commercially viable until the third year, reaching full production in the fifth year. In the past pollarding was not done at ground level but at about 1.8 metres (6 feet) above ground, so that the young and tasty shoots would be well out of reach of grazing stock. Nowadays animals can be kept well away from the osier plantations and all stages of the production of this crop are mechanised.

Fig. 13. *An osier bed being hoed. Notice the straight unbranched shoots rising from a crown cut close to the ground.*

These cut willows are fast growing and may produce shoots of 2 to 2.5 metres (6 feet 6 inches to 8 feet 3 inches) in one year. The untreated rods are called 'brown' and are sometimes sold like this, but usually they are treated and peeled by one of two methods to produce 'white' or 'buff' rods. To make them white, the rods are stood in shallow water until the buds are about to burst open. The bark is then peeled off, either by hand or by machine. To obtain rods that are a more reddish brown colour, they are boiled before the bark is removed. Chemicals present in the bark, such as tannins, stain the wood. After either of these treatments the rods are dried and are then ready for use.

A local variant of willow basketry is the Sussex 'trug', which is made from larger willow poles that are cleft into fairly thin strips. These are steamed so that they can be bent to shape and fitted into a rim of another wood such as sweet chestnut. Trugs are serviceable boat-shaped baskets and are still made.

Fig. 14. *'Cutting the splice', a stage in the skilled craft of cricket bat manufacture.*

FURTHER READING

Many aspects of willow life history and ecology have of necessity been only briefly described here. Little mention has been made of non-British species, some of which hybridise with the native British willows, and their cultivars. Most of these have been introduced to Britain because they possess some attractive feature, such as brightly coloured stems or catkins, distinctive foliage or an unusual growth form, and descriptions of them may be found in gardening books and horticultural catalogues. The three introduced species included in Tables 1 and 2 were an exception, as they are very frequently encountered in gardens. The Weeping Willow merits special mention, because of its popularity and because it is an interesting hybrid.

For keys and a more detailed account of each native species it is recommended that *Willows and Poplars of Great Britain and Ireland* by R. D. Meikle (BSBI Handbook number 4, 1984) and *Flora of the British Isles* by A. R. Clapham, T. G. Tutin and E. F. Warburg (Cambridge University Press, 1962) be consulted. An extensive account of all recorded hybrids between these species is furnished by R. D. Meikle in *Hybridisation and the Flora of the British Isles* (edited by C. A. Stace). Many books in Collins' 'New Naturalist' series contain interesting information about the ecology of willows. Other books recommended are:

Hora, B. (editor). *The Oxford Encyclopedia of Trees of the World.* Oxford University Press, 1981.

Mitchell, A. *A Field Guide to the Trees of Britain and Northern Europe.* Collins, 1974.

Phillips, R. *Trees in Britain, Europe and North America.* Pan, 1978.

Tansley, Sir A. G. *The British Isles and their Vegetation.* Cambridge University Press, 1949.

ACKNOWLEDGEMENTS

The author wishes to thank Dr D. H. Dalby for providing Figure 12; the Institute of Agricultural History and the Museum of English Rural Life, University of Reading, for Figures 13 and 14; and P. H. Ward (Natural Science Photos) for Plate 16. All other illustrations are by the author.